SIMPSONS COMICS
BIG BONANZA

TITAN BOOKS

To the loving memory of Snowball I:
You are missed every day because we can't
find your burial marker in the backyard.

SIMPSONS COMICS BIG BONANZA

Copyright ©1991,1993,1997 & 1998 by
Bongo Entertainment, Inc. All rights reserved.

FIRST EDITION: FEBRUARY 1999

ISBN 1-84023-058-4

2 4 6 8 10 9 7 5 3 1

Publisher: MATT GROENING
Art Director / Editor: BILL MORRISON
Managing Editor: TERRY DELEGEANE
Director of Operations: ROBERT ZAUGH
Book Design: MARILYN FRANDSEN
Legal Guardian: SUSAN GRODE

Contributing Artists:
KAREN BATES, TIM BAVINGTON, JEANNINE BLACK, CHRIS CLEMENTS,
STEPHANIE GLADDEN, TIM HARKINS, CARL HARMON, NATHAN KANE,
BILL MORRISON, JULIUS PREITE, PHIL ORTIZ, STEVE STEERE, JR.,
CHRISTOPHER UNGAR, CINDY VANCE, STEVE VANCE

Contributing Writers:
SCOTT M. GIMPLE, GARY GLASBERG, JIM LINCOLN, BILL MORRISON,
JEFF ROSENTHAL, DAN STUDNEY, CINDY VANCE, STEVE VANCE, ROB WALTON

CONTENTS

SIMPSONS #28

- 8   Krustonia
- 29   Flanders' Big Score

SIMPSONS #29

- 36   Let's Get Ready To Bumble!
- 57   Bringing Down Baby
- 63   Otto's Top 40

SIMPSONS #30

- 66   Smitherses!
- 87   Bore Us - The Movie - Gruel
- 92   Lisa's Dream House

SIMPSONS #31

- 96   Radioactive Homer
- 118   Comic Convention Survival Guide

A BRIE-BURGER WITH CAPERS, WORCESTERSHIRE, AND SPINACH ON A BRUSSELS SPROUT BUN! *NOW* WE'LL START GETTIN' THE *OPERA CROWD* THROUGH THE DOOR!

I JUST CAN'T KEEP IT DOWN.

THEY LAUGHED AT KRYSTAL KRUSTY KOLA BUT WE'RE GONNA HAVE THE LAST GAS ON THIS ONE! THE KRUST DELUXE IS THE BURGER OF THE *FUTURE!*

CLAP! CLAP! CLAP!

MMMM.

SO THAT'S IT, RIGHT? I GOTTA GET TO THE LINKS.

THE NEXT ITEM ON THE AGENDA REGARDS PAYING YOUR *TAXES*, KRUSTY.

OH YEAH, WE'RE ACTUALLY DOING THAT THIS YEAR, HUH?

WHAT?

I COULDN'T *BELIEVE* WHAT I HEARD. IT WAS LIKE SOMEONE JUST TOLD ME THAT CHRISTMAS WAS CANCELED AND CREAM PIES HAD GONE OFF THE MARKET. AND *THAT'S* WHERE IT ALL STARTED.

KRUSTY, THERE'S NO OTHER WAY! YOU MAY BE THE JOLTIN' JOE OF JOLLY, BUT YOU'RE NO MATCH FOR *THE IRS!* THIS YEAR YOU HAVE TO *PLAY IT STRAIGHT!*

BUT I CAN STILL COUNT MR. TEENY AS A DEPENDENT, RIGHT?

YOU HAD TO COMMIT *MASSIVE INSURANCE FRAUD* TO GET YOURSELF OUT OF YOUR *LAST SCRAPE* WITH THE TAX MAN AND YOU CAN ILL-AFFORD ANY MORE FINES WITH ALL YOUR ASSETS TIED INTO THE PROMOTION OF THE KRUST DELUXE!

YOU HAVE TO PAY YOUR TAXES THIS YEAR WITHOUT ANY *FUNNY BUSINESS*--

THAT MEANS NO MORE FAKING YOUR DEATH IN PLANE CRASHES!

FELLAS, IF THERE'S ONE THING I'VE LEARNED ON THIS WILD RIDE TO THE STRATOSPHERE, IT'S THAT *THERE'S A WAY AROUND ANYTHING.* NOW I'M GOING TO SIT HERE, LOOSEN THE STRINGS ON MY SHOES, AND ONE OF YOU IS GOING TO TELL ME HOW WE'RE HOLDING ONTO THE COOKIE JAR THIS YEAR.

NONE OF YOU HAVE ANY IDEAS?? *NONE OF YOU??* THEY'RE GONNA TAKE IT ALL AWAY AGAIN! OH, GAWD!! OH GAWD!!!

WELL, THERE WAS THAT *LITTLE BOY* WHO EXPOSED THE OFFSHORE BANK ACCOUNT YOU USED TO HIDE UNTOLD MILLIONS FROM THE FEDERAL GOVERNMENT. *HE* SEEMED TO KNOW HIS WAY AROUND THE TAX CODES!

GET HIM!

SLAM!

HI, I'M *TROY MCCLURE*. YOU MAY REMEMBER ME FROM *OTHER* CORPORATE-SPONSORED EDUCATIONAL TELEVISION SEGMENTS LIKE "*SHELLRON'S COLONIALISM SHAMOLONIALISM-- WE CALL IT WORK*" AND "*SCHEVITZCO'S 16 MINUTES ON THE MEANING OF MATZOH*."

TODAY, I BRING YOU THE TALE OF THE FORMATION OF A RUNTY COUNTRY THAT TURNED INTO *ONE HECK* OF A NATION, *THE UNITED STATES*. AND IT ALL STARTED BECAUSE OF A LITTLE SOMETHING CALLED *TAXES*.

FORTY MINUTES LATER...

HMMM...ALL THAT TALK ABOUT THE *TEA PARTY'S* MADE ME *THIRSTY*. BOY, COULD I GO FOR A NICE, ICY GLASS OF *NESCATEA* RIGHT NOW!

I'LL HAVE TO *PAY* SOME *SALES TAX* ON THAT -- BUT AT LEAST I KNOW I'M *REPRESENTED IN CONGRESS*. I'M TROY MCCLURE. THANKS FOR WATCHING!

ALL RIGHT CHILDREN, TIME FOR RECESS. CANS OF NESCATEA WILL BE AVAILABLE FOR PURCHASE OUT BY THE JUNGLE GYM.

THIS SUCKS. EVERY TIME WE BUY AN ISH OF RADIOACTIVE MAN, *TWENTY CENTS* GOES TO THE GOVERNMENT, AND DO WE SEE ANY OF THOSE *FAT CAT POLITICOS* GIVING A RIP ABOUT *OUR* CONCERNS?

C'MON BART! SHHHH!

14

I JUST DON'T KNOW ABOUT THIS, HOMEY.

MAAARGE! THAT INFOMERCIAL *SPOKE* TO ME! IT'S BEEN MY LIFELONG DREAM TO LEAVE AMERICA BEHIND TO FIND A *LAND OF OPPORTUNITY!*

I THOUGHT YOUR LIFELONG DREAM WAS TO HAVE A *CHEESE* NAMED AFTER YOU! REMEMBER?

OH, I *REMEMBER!* I REMEMBER SIRENS AND LIGHTS! MILK SPLASHED AGAINST A RED BRICK WALL! THE TRIAL! THE *RESTRAINING ORDER* FROM THE DAIRY! OH, I REMEMBER MARGE! YES, I REMEMBER IT *WELL!*

BESIDES, MOM, A *VOTE IS A VOTE!* THREE FOR, YOU AGAINST, MAGGIE ABSTAINING.

I'M SORRY, BUT THIS COULD BE A CHANCE TO BE A PART OF *HISTORY--* TO WELCOME A BRAVE, NEW WORLD INTO EXISTENCE!!

I'M GOING TO NAME MY PONY *ALDOUS.*

LET'S SEE HOW MANY CHUMPS SHOWED UP...

HOLY JOE TOLEDO...

HEEEEY CITIZENS! I...UH..ER..

I'LL BE BACK IN A SECOND.

UH, OH...

WHAT AM I GONNA DO?? I THOUGHT I'D JUST BE PUTTING UP *THREE WACKOS* IN THE *TOOL SHED!* I GOT *TWENTY PEOPLE* OUT THERE!

THERE'S *STILL TIME* TO CALL THIS OFF, KRUSTY! IT'S NOT TOO LATE.

UHHHHH...

WHAT ABOUT YOUR *POSTERS*, KRUSTY? WHAT ABOUT YOUR *PROFESSIONALLY PRODUCED INFOMERCIAL*? WHAT ABOUT THE *MANIFESTO* YOU PRINTED UP ON THE BACK OF YOUR *LI'L KRUSTER MEALS*?

I KNOW, KID. BUT I WASN'T IN THIS FOR A *HASSLE*; I JUST WANTED--

YOU SAID YOU WANTED TO LIVE ANOTHER WAY-- *THE KRUSTY WAY*--AND PEOPLE *LISTENED!* YOU CAN DO IT, KRUSTY! YOU CAN MAKE YOUR *TAX-FREE DREAM* COME *TRUE!*

THOSE WORDS RANG IN MY EARS. "TAX FREE"... I KNEW THERE WAS ONLY *ONE CHOICE*...

THE KID'S *RIGHT!*

17

OKAY! *SIDESHOW MEL,* GO WITH MR. TEENY AND PACK UP THE STUDIO--FROM NOW ON, WE'RE SHOOTIN' THE SHOW *HERE!*

CORPORAL PUNISHMENT, GET OUR TRAILERS OUT HERE AND FIX 'EM UP FOR *MY PEOPLE*-- THAT MEANS TAKE OUT THE YOU- KNOW-WHAT-GRAPHY!

MS. PENNYCANDY! GET ME OL' MAN GIBBERSON AT THE DISCOUNT INDUSTRIAL FEED N' SEED WAREHOUSE! I NEED *FOOD* FOR MY PEOPLE!

WHY NOT FEED 'EM KRUSTYBURGERS?

I NEED SOMETHIN' *CHEAP!* I GOT A COUPLE DOZEN PEOPLE OUT THERE!

CHEAPER THAN KRUSTYBURGERS?

AND MEL, STOP BY CLUCKY'S CAMERAS ON YOUR WAY BACK! YOU'RE GONNA MAKE A PICTURE-- BUT NOT THAT STUPID BIOPIC ON PAUL LYNDE--YOU'RE GONNA DOCUMENT THE START OF THE GREATEST COUNTRY THE WORLD HAS EVER SEEN! YOU'RE GONNA FILM *"THE MIRTH OF A NATION: THE STORY OF KRUSTYLVANIA!"*

YOU MEAN *KRUSTONIA.*

WHATEVER! WE'LL MAKE SOME *MOOLA* ON THIS YET!

OKAY, SO WE'RE HAVING A LITTLE *SECESSION* SITUATION HERE... WE DON'T WANT TO DO ANYTHING TOO *HASTY* NOW, BOYS. THE BEST WAY TO DO THIS IS TO WAIT 'EM OUT...STEADY AS SHE GOES.

NOW, WHO BROUGHT THE UNO?

SHELTER-- CHECK.

STAY AWAKE WITH KENT

THE KRUSTY THE KLOWN SHOW

MY DAD IS A CLOWN!

I TELL YA, I GOT SHELTER COMIN' OUT MY *EARS*! THOSE ONES OVER THERE HAVE BEEN SITTIN' SINCE THE NETWORK CANNED MY *MIDSEASON REPLACEMENT*.

I'M *SORRY* ABOUT GETTING LARRY KICKED OUT OF THE DANCE. IT'S JUST, WELL, I'VE NEVER BEEN A *CHAPERONE* BEFORE. I GUESS I JUST GOT A LITTLE *CARRIED AWAY*.

IT'S OKAY, DAD. BUT YOU JUST GOTTA REALIZE THAT I'M NOT A *LITTLE KID* ANYMORE. *OKAY*?

OKAY. NOW GET YOUR JAMMIES ON AND I'LL TUCK YOU IN. *KIDDING! KIDDING!*

FOOD, CHE--

HEY, HEY, HEY! WHAT'S GOIN' ON HERE?

LOOK--EVERYBODY GETS ONE *SOY-LITE SALAMI* AND ONE *HEAD OF KALE* A DAY UNTIL THE FUNNY SOUNDING VEGETABLES START GROWING--CAPICE? WE'RE IN THIS TOGETHER, PEOPLE!

BUT THIS ONE WAS *EXTRA*!

FINE, SHARE IT... *CUT IT IN HALF.*

I WAS REALLY GETTIN' INTO THE *KING-THING*. WHAT CAN I SAY? I WAS *GOOD* AT IT. IT MADE ME FEEL THE SAME WAY I DID WHEN I HIT THAT TRIFECTA FOR *SIXTY G'S* AT SPRINGFIELD DOWNS BACK IN '78. BUT THE FEELING WAS STICKIN', AND *I* DIDN'T HAVE TO HAVE ANY JOCKEYS *ROUGHED UP* TO GET IT.

SO, FRINK, WILL IT *WORK*?

I HAVE NO DOUBT THAT THIS, ЗGAЇ, SOLUTION WHICH I'VE DEVISED WILL...ЗGRЇ...SPEED THE PLANTS' GROWING TIME *EXPONENTIALLY*. EITHER THAT OR IT WILL RENDER THIS ENTIRE PLOT A FIELD OF...ЗGRЇ...*DEATH*. BUT THE CHANCES OF THE LATTER OCCURRING IS...ЗGRRЇ... *QUITE MARGINAL*.

PEOPLE STARTED COMIN' TO ME FOR *GUIDANCE*. I GAVE THEM *DIRECTION*, I *INSPIRED* THEM, I *SETTLED THEIR DISPUTES*...

LESS FILLING.

WOO HOO! *IN YOUR FACE*, GUMBLE!

AND THEN, WHEN I TAPED THE SHOW, I'D MAKE 'EM *LAUGH*. WHEN WAS THE LAST TIME THE QUEEN OF ENGLAND NAILED THE OL' *'THROW YOUR SIDEKICK INTO A BRICK WALL'* GAG?

LIVE FROM KRUSTONIA!

WHAM!

I'LL TELL YA WHEN -- THE LAST TIME WAS OVER 400 YEARS AGO WHEN ELIZABETH I WAS IN POWER WITH THE HOUSE OF TUDOR. AND SHE *BOTCHED* THE TOSS.

HOW DO I LOOK, KID?

LIKE A *MILLION TAX-FREE BUCKS*, OH SOVEREIGN OF YUCKS!

THANKS.

WE HAD HIT OUR STRIDE. ALL THOSE CHUMPS WITH THE BADGES AND THE MEGAPHONES COULD *DANGLE* ... WHEN IT STARTED, IT WAS A *JOKE*--BUT *NOT ANYMORE*. KRUSTONIA WAS A *REALITY*. I THOUGHT NOTHING COULD STOP US.

THAT WAS MY BIGGEST MISTAKE.

WHM!

KRUSTY!!!

YOU DON'T HAVE AN APPOINTME--

I CAME HERE BECAUSE YOU SAID THIS PLACE WOULD BE LIKE A *COUNTRY CLUB*-- INSTEAD I'M PLOWING FIELDS WAITING FOR *RHUBARB* TO GROW!

I WANT *OUT*-- AND I'M TAKING *MY FAMILY* WITH ME!

I WENT *NUTS*. I COULDN'T LOSE VAN HOUTEN! WHAT IF THE OTHERS STARTED *LININ' UP* BEHIND HIM? I HADDA KEEP EVERYTHING *JAKE*.

YOU CAN'T GO! YOU'RE IN *TOO DEEP*, VAN HOUTEN!

GO TELL IT TO YOUR *MONKEY*, CLOWN BOY.

HE'S A CHIMP!!

GAAAAAAAH!!!

WHAT CAN I SAY? I'M A *PASSIONATE MAN*.

AHEM...EXCELLENT! IT **WORKS!**

YOU 'VOLUNTEERS' WILL BE PROVIDING POWER FOR HIS MAJESTICNESS' BROADCAST. YOU SHOULD FEEL **HONORED**.

'VOLUNTEERS!' YOU FORCED US INTO THIS FOR **QUESTIONING** KRUSTY!

WOW, I'M LOSIN' FEELIN' IN MY HEELS...

OH, JUST WAIT FRINK...YOU'LL KNOW PAYBACK! **YOU'LL KNOW PAYBACK!**

OH, I...WOO HOY...WOULDN'T **COUNT** ON IT, BALPHAZAR. I STILL WIELD THE TRILCANI DEVICE. YOU WOULDN'T **DARE** RAISE A HAND AGAINST ME!

WE'RE THE FCC. **WATCH IT THERE, PALLY.**

LIVE FROM **KRUSTONIA!** IT'S **THE KRUSTY THE KLOWN SHOW!**

WHERE THE &*#@ ARE THE **TROPICO BIKINI FINALS?** WAITAMINUTE! WHAT THE &*#@ IS THIS &*#@?

CLICK!

GET ME THE *#@!! CHAIRMAN!

THE NETWORK IS **DROPPING** US??

THEY SAY THEY CAN'T BROADCAST FOREIGN-OWNED PROGRAMMING UNLESS YOU BECOME AN AUSTRALIAN CITIZEN AND A MEMBER OF THE REPUBLICAN PARTY.

FORGET IT! I'VE ALREADY **GOT** A COUNTRY.

I DIDN'T CARE. I WAS **BIGGER** THAN A CRUMMY T.V. SHOW!

I WAS A NOBLE, GODLY FORCE SHEPHERDING MY PEOPLE TOWARDS **PEACE, STABILITY,** AND **ENLIGHTEN-MENT!** I WENT DOWN THE HILL TO DELIVER THE MAIL.

UH, HEEEEEY CITIZENS!

HERE, KID. YOU GOT A LETTER. I, UH...

...UHHHHHH...

I DIDN'T KNOW WHAT TO DO. MY PEOPLE WERE LOOKING AT ME LIKE THE *CATSKILLS CROWD* THAT NIGHT I ACCIDENTALLY LIT RED BUTTONS ON FIRE.

WHO THE--

SEYMOUR SKINNER, FORMER *SERGEANT*, U.S. ARMY, CURRENT *PRINCIPAL* OF SPRINGFIELD ELEMENTARY. IT SEEMS AS THOUGH ONE OF KRUSTY'S "CITIZENS" HAS SOMETHING THAT *BELONGS TO ME*.

AND WHAT MIGHT THAT BE?

THE SPRINGFIELD ELEMENTARY LIBRARY'S COPY OF "THE GREAT BRAIN AT APPAMATOX." THE PERP: ONE *LISA SIMPSON*.

AND NOW, GENTLEMEN, IF YOU'LL *STEP ASIDE*, I HAVE A COUNTRY TO *OVERTHROW* AND A DELIGHTFUL NOVEL ABOUT A PRECOCIOUS LITTLE LAD CAUGHT IN THE CIVIL WAR TO *RETURN* TO THE CHILDREN OF SPRINGFIELD.

CITIZENS OF KRUSTONIA, LEND ME YOUR EAR! WE'RE *STILL* IN THIS *TOGETHER!* KRUSTY *KNOWS* YOU DON'T HAVE ELECTRICITY FOR THE LAUNDRY MACHINE!

HE *KNOWS* YOU FEEL *SICK* FROM LIVING OFF THE SAME STRANGE-TASTING FOOD FOR SEVERAL WEEKS! HE *KNOWS* YOU'RE ALL SCARED THAT HE'S BECOMING A *TOTALITARIAN DESPOT!* BUT...

HMMM...I WAS GOING SOMEWHERE WITH THIS.

EVERYBODY LISTEN! I SENT AWAY FOR THE NUTRITIONAL INFORMATION! SOY-LITE SALAMIS ARE TADPOLES!! THEY'RE TADPOLES!!

IT WOULD'VE BEEN SO BEAUTIFUL.

THAT'S IT! I'M SICK OF THIS LOUSY COUNTRY! THERE'S *NO T.V.* ANYMORE, THERE'S *NO LEGISLATURE*, AND THE SALAMIS AREN'T MADE OF *SALAMI STUFF!* LET'S GET KRUSTY!!

YEAH!!

A HEAVEN ON EARTH.

ONWARD, MUGS! GLORY AWAITS!

WHAM!

THOSE HORRIBLE, HORRIBLE SALAMIS...

CALL FOR THE CAR.

PHONE THE *ACCOUNTANTS*, MRS. PENNYCANDY. HAVE THEM SEND *THE CHECK* TO THE IRS.

KRUSTY, WE DO HAVE IT ALL ON FILM.

OY.

MONTHS LATER...

FLANDERS BIG SCORE

A NED FLANDERS MYSTERY

HEY-DILLY-HO, *MYSTERY MAVENS!* THE NAME'S *FLANDERS* BUT SOME FOLKS CALL ME *NED!* TO OTHERS I'M KNOWN AS NEDDY, DAD, DA-DIDDLE-ADDY, MR. F., AND FOR SOME STRANGE REASON, THE LOCAL POLICE INSIST ON CALLING ME HUGGY-BEAR! BUT NO MATTER THE HANDLE, I'M ALWAYS READY TO ANSWER WHEN TROUBLE CALLS MY NAME... *ESPECIALLY* THE LORD'S TROUBLE!

THIS PARTICULAR LITTLE PICKLE STARTED ONE AFTERNOON AT THE SPRINGFIELD COMMUNITY CHURCH. I HAD ARRIVED A TEENSY BIT LATE FOR AN IMPORTANT COMMITTEE MEETING. OUR MISSION: PUT THE *'FUN'* BACK IN *FUND-RAISER!*

LISTEN UP, FOLKS. IT'S TIME FOR OUR ANNUAL "I AM *THAT* I *AMBROSIA*" COOK-OFF! AS USUAL, WE NEED TO LAY IN A TREMENDOUS SUPPLY OF PINK GELATIN, MAYONNAISE, AND TINY MARSHMALLOWS.

MMM...AMBROSIA! SO PINK... SO GOOPY...

THANKS BE TO GOD FOR A *HEALTHY CHURCH TREASURY* AND A *BULKRAGEOUS BIG BUYERS CLUB* MEMBER-SHIP CARD!

GOOD LORD ⁞CHOKE⁞ WE'VE BEEN ROBBED.

BULK BUYERS
MEMBERSHIP CARD

Jim J. & Tammy Jay Fan Club

LET'S NOT PANIC PEOPLE. IT JUST SO HAPPENS THAT A MEMBER OF OUR OWN FLOCK IS QUALIFIED TO INVESTIGATE THIS HEINOUS CRIME. IT SEEMS LIKE JUST THE OTHER DAY...

"...WHEN I HANDED THAT *DETECTIVE CORRESPONDENCE COURSE* OVER TO NED FLANDERS AT THE CHARITY AUCTION WE HELD TO BUY BARNEY GUMBLE A NEW LIVER..."

WITH *THIS*, I'LL BE ABLE TO FERRET OUT THE RASCAL THAT'S BEEN CLIPPING THE *DOUGHNUT COUPONS* OUT OF OUR *SUNDAY PAPER!*

PRISON PASTELS

HYPNOHEAD'S
MIND CONTROL KIT

DAVE 'MR. SNOOPY' NAGELMAN'S DETECTIVE CORRESPONDENCE KIT

DUFF HOME BREWERY

"...BEFORE LONG, HE BECAME A TOP-NOTCH PRIVATE RICHARD."

YES INDEEDLY, REVEREND! NED FLANDERS, PRIVATE EYE IS ON THE CASE.

OOH!

WHOA!

AND THE FIRST CLUE TO FINDING THE THIEF IS THIS *UNMARKED KEY* THAT JUST DROPPED OUT OF THE *COLLECTION KITTY.* I'D BETTER DUST THIS LIL' BEAUTY FOR PRINTS!

SCRIPT GARY GLASBERG   *PENCILS* PHIL ORTIZ   *INKS* TIM HARKINS   *LETTERS* JEANNINE BLACK   *COLORS* NATHAN KANE   *USUAL SUSPECT* MATT GROENING

I INFORMED OUR MEN IN BLUE THAT I WAS ON THE CASE, WORKING ON BEHALF OF THE ALMIGHTY. BUT IT WAS CLEAR THE CHIEF DIDN'T WANT *YOURS TRULY* SNIFFING AROUND.

CHIEF WIGGUM

NO WAY! FORGET IT, FLANDERS! THIS IS *MY JURISDICTION* AND I WILL NOT STAND BY AND WATCH YOU *SCREW UP* MY INVESTIGATION.

WELL, OKILY-DOKILY. BUT WILL A WARM AND TASTY BEAR CLAW CONVINCE YOU?

OH, *PAYOLA*, EH?

WHY DIDN'T YOU *SAY* SO?

DONUTS

DONUT

I BEGAN TO QUESTION ANYONE THAT HAD ACCESS TO THE CHURCH ON A REGULAR BASIS. MY KEEN INSTINCTS TOLD ME THAT THIS WAS AN *INSIDE JOB*.

ALRIGHTY-DIGHTY, MY TWO LITTLE BAMBINOS. LISTEN CAREFULLY. DO CHOIR BOYS EVER *STEAL* FROM THE *COLLECTION PLATE* AT CHURCH?

GAAAAAHHH! THAT WOULD BE A HARBINGER OF *THE APOCALYPSE!*

YEEEEEEK! SUCH THINGS CAN'T BE POSSIBLE!

BUT AS THE DAY WENT ON, THE INNOCENT FOLKS STARTED TO OUTNUMBER THE GUILTY ONES.

WELL SIR, MR. GUMBLE, HAVE YOU GOT SOMETHING TO CONFESS?

YOU GOTTA BELIEVE ME, FLANDERS!

THAT CASE OF COMMUNION WINE WAS EMPTY WHEN I *GOT* THERE!

⸨SOB⸩ PLEASE STOP -- I CAN'T STAND *PLAIN WATER!*

I COULDN'T UNCOVER A SINGLE DANG-DIDDLEY CLUE! I WAS READY TO COZY UP WITH THIS MONTH'S *MODERN WHITTLING* AND CALL IT A NIGHT WHEN --

RATA-TAT-TAT!

SCREECH!

RATTA-TA-TA-TA-TAT!

IT WAS OBVIOUS SOMEBODY *DIDN'T* WANT ME *SNOOPING AROUND*. MANAGING TO AVOID MEETING MY MAKER, I KISSED MY DASHBOARD DAVEY AND GOLIATH AND QUICKLY JOTTED DOWN THE ASSAILANT'S LICENSE PLATE.

SISTUHS

I NEEDED TO RUN THAT PLATE, SO I CALLED THE CHIEF FROM AN OUT OF THE WAY GREASY SPOON AND MADE HIS TUMMY AN OFFER IT COULDN'T REFUSE: *THREE PLATES OF BACON* AND A *LEMON TODDY!*

:SMACK: THAT'S SOME *MIGHTY FINE TODDY,* FLANDERS! THANKS! :GLOMPH: HERE'S THAT AUTO REGISTRATION THINGY YOU WANTED.

WOW...WELL, *PLUCK MY PERSIMMONS!*

"SISTUHS" WAS REGISTERED TO *PATTY AND SELMA BOUVIER.* THEY WERE TWO GALS WHO WERE *OBVIOUSLY* CONCERNED ABOUT THEIR APPEARANCE. *I* WAS, TOO--THAT NIGHT, I WOULD PRAY FOR THEM. IT TURNED OUT THEY HAD A *PEACH* OF AN ALIBI.

WHAT DO YOU MEAN YOU TWO WEREN'T *DRIVING* THAT CAR?!

YOU HEARD US, NERD BOY. THAT OLD BOMB WAS *STOLEN* LAST WEEK AND WE HAVEN'T SEEN IT SINCE.

WE'VE GOT THE POLICE REPORT TO PROVE IT, SO *GET LOST,* COLOMBO!

WHOEVER STOLE THE CHURCH COLLECTION MONEY CLEARLY KNEW HOW TO COVER THEIR TRACKS. I NEEDED A LACTOSE-REDUCED DOUBLE CHOCOLATE SODA TO SOOTHE MY FRAZZLED NERVES, AND APU'S FLUORESCENT LIGHTS CALLED TO ME LIKE A LONELY BEACON. I FEARED THIS WOULD BE MY FIRST UNSOLVED CASE WHEN A *MIRACLE* HAPPENED.

BLESS MY BLOOMERS!

UNFORTUNATELY, I CANNOT ALLOW YOU TO SEE THE TAPE WITHOUT THE EXPRESS WRITTEN PERMISSION OF *KWIK-E-MART INTERNATIONAL.*

APU, THAT SECURITY CAMERA'S POINTED STRAIGHT AT MY BULLET RIDDLED JALOPY. IT *MAY* HAVE PHOTOGRAPHED THE ATTACKER IN THE ACT!

TELL ME SOMETHING, NEIGHBOR. WHEN WAS THE LAST TIME THE *HEALTH INSPECTOR* HAD A LOOK-SEE AT YOUR *NACHO CHEESE DISPENSER?*

EEP! WOULD YOU BE PREFERRING BETA, VHS, OR PERHAPS A TRANSFER TO CD-ROM?

THE DRIVER'S A NUN? A *NUN*?!? BUT SHE TRIED TO SNUFF ME OUT IN A HAIL OF *WHITE-HOT LEAD!*

WELCOME TO MY WORLD, SIR.

BUT THERE WERE NO NUNS *IN* OUR CHURCH. I'D HIT ANOTHER DANG-DIDDLY DEAD-END...

...SO I DECIDED TO HAVE A POW-WOW WITH REVEREND LOVEJOY.

MY PEEPERS *DON'T LIE*, REVEREND! I SAW A *NUN'S HABIT*, PLAIN AS DAY!

THERE HASN'T BEEN A NUN AROUND HERE SINCE *ST. ABERNATHY'S* PICKETED US FOR *UNFAIR COMPETITION*.

REMEMBER WHEN WE GAVE OUT FREE SNOW TIRES WITH EACH CHRISTENING?

I SPENT THAT NIGHT WAITING FOR A SIGN FROM THE ALMIGHTY. SUDDENLY, IT CAME TO ME IN THE FORM OF A YELLOW TWO-DOOR. I FOLLOWED THE SPEED DEMON IN HOT PURSUIT!

SCREECH!

Highlights MAGAZINE

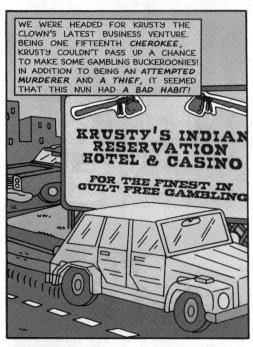

WE WERE HEADED FOR KRUSTY THE CLOWN'S LATEST BUSINESS VENTURE. BEING ONE FIFTEENTH *CHEROKEE*, KRUSTY COULDN'T PASS UP A CHANCE TO MAKE SOME GAMBLING BUCKEROONIES! IN ADDITION TO BEING AN *ATTEMPTED MURDERER* AND A *THIEF*, IT SEEMED THAT THIS NUN HAD A *BAD HABIT!*

KRUSTY'S INDIAN RESERVATION HOTEL & CASINO

FOR THE FINEST IN GUILT FREE GAMBLING

THE SISTER SEEMED AS COMFORTABLE TOSSING THE BONES AS ANY AGING HOUSEWIFE LOOKING FOR A CHEAP THRILL IN TAHOE. APPARENTLY, SHE WAS PARLAYING OUR COLLECTION MONEY INTO A SMALL FORTUNE!

YAY!

WOO-HOO!

YIPPEE!

SLIP MOTHER THERESA THE *LOADED* DICE. SHE'S WIPIN' US OUT!

THE TIME HAD COME TO MAKE MY MOVE. *GOLLY-GOSHEROO*, I HAD THE NUN CORNERED WITH *THE CASH!*

PRESIDENTIAL SUITE

CLICK!

SWOOSH!

THE KEY I PICKED UP IN THE CHURCH REC ROOM FIT THE HOTEL DOOR *PERFECTLY!*

THE END.

I GAVE MAN *FIRE* FOR A *REASON*. SO HE COULD *BARBECUE!* SO BRING THE FAMILY OUT TO FEAST ON MY AWARD-WINNING SHISH KEBAB OR TO PECK AT MY LIVER, IT'S *MYTHICALLY* DELICIOUS!

PROMETHEUS GREEK BBQ

CLICK!

EVERY CHANNEL I TURNED TO *TAUNTED* ME.

YOKI, LULA, COME *BACK* HERE! IN THE NAME OF ALL THAT IS HOLY, BOB, PUT THE FREAKIN' CAMERA *DOWN* AND GET THIS MONSTER *OFF* OF ME!

HURRY! MUST FIND SOMETHING TO FRY OR BROIL. GRILL OR... MMM... CARAMELIZE.

I *TRIED* TO HOLD OUT, BUT I'M TOO *WEAK*, MARGE.

THE NEXT THING I KNEW I WAS FIXING A COUPLE OF *ITSY-BITSY* LATE NIGHT SNACKS. I'LL CLEAN THIS MESS UP, MARGE-- I PROMISE.

IT'S NOT THE MESS THAT WORRIES ME, HOMER.

YOU ARE *TOO EASILY* INFLUENCED BY WHAT YOU SEE ON *LATE NIGHT TV.*

BUT, MARGE, WHEN IT'S ON *TV* IT SEEMS SO *IMPORTANT!*

AAARRH! AHOY THERE, ALL YOU SEAFOOD LOVIN' WRESTLIN' FANS. I'M HERE TO TELL YA ALL ABOUT THE *UNIVERSAL WRESTLING ASSOCIATION'S* "EAT-AND-GREET" AT *THE FRYIN' DUTCHMAN* T'MORROW NIGHT. YER BOUND TO ENJOY EATIN' MUSSELS AS THE MUSCLE-BOUND LIKES O' *THE PUNISHING PILGRIM* TAKE ON THAT CHAMPION O' CHAMPIONS, *CAPT. SLAMTASTIC!*

WOO HOO!! MARGE, REV. LOVEJOY WAS *RIGHT!* PRAYERS *DO* GET ANSWERED! TOMORROW NIGHT I'M TREATING MY FAMILY TO *WRESTLING* AND *SURF AND TURF!!*

TOMORROW NIGHT *I'M* TAKING THE KIDS TO PATTY AND SELMA'S HOUSE FOR DINNER. YOU CAN MAKE *THIS* FOR YOURSELF AND STAY HOME ALONE TO THINK ABOUT WHAT YOU'VE DONE.

YES, DEAR.

Angela Lansbury's *Dinner, She Cooked* tonight's meal *Mystery Meat*

I CAN'T BELIEVE IT, I'VE CREATED A WIN-WIN SITUATION.

MARTY, IT SEEMS AS IF CAPT. SLAMTASTIC IS ABOUT TO LOSE THE FIRST MATCH OF HIS ILLUSTRIOUS CAREER!

IT SURE LOOKS THAT WAY, BILL. THE DUKE OF DOOM HAS CAPT. SLAMTASTIC IN HIS WORLD RENOWNED *"ATOMIC ADAM'S APPLE SMASHER!"*

BOO! HISS!

WELL, MARTY, IN THE PRE-FIGHT INTERVIEW THE DUKE PROMISED HE'D TURN CAPT. SLAMTASTIC INTO *"DOOM'S BROOM"* AND SWEEP THE *FLOOR* WITH HIM.

I JUST DON'T KNOW WHERE THESE WRESTLER'S COME UP WITH SUCH CREATIVE NAMES FOR THEIR MOVES.

BOO!

OH, BOY! THE CROWD CERTAINLY WASN'T EXPECTING *THIS* KIND OF AN UPSET. ONE CAN ONLY IMAGINE WHAT IS GOING THROUGH THE MIND OF CAPT. SLAMTASTIC.

OH, NO! I DON'T *BELIEVE* THIS...

...I FORGOT TO SET MY VCR TO TAPE *ED ASNER IN "KING LEAR"* ON THE ARTS AND INFOTAINMENT CHANNEL.

WHAT AN UNBELIEVABLE TURN OF EVENTS! THIS KIND OF LAST MINUTE VICTORY ALMOST *NEVER* HAPPENS IN WRESTLING.

I'LL SAY! IT'S THE BIGGEST COMEBACK SINCE A CERTAIN FORMER "SWEATHOG" DID *THE BATUSI* AND MADE CINEMATIC HISTORY!

HURRAY!

YEAH!

THE NEXT DAY...

YOU RANG, MR. BURNS?

THAT WOULD BE *"OMPHALOSKEPSIS,"* SIR.

AH, SMITHERS, JUST IN THE NICK OF TIME. THIS "WORD SCRAMBLER" HAS ME SIMPLY BEFUDDLED. WHAT'S A FOURTEEN LETTER WORD FOR THE CONTEMPLATION OF ONE'S NAVEL?

EXCELLENT! ANOTHER BRAIN TICKLER SOLVED. SMITHERS, WHAT'S NEXT ON MY AFTERNOON SCHEDULE. IS IT TIME FOR MY RUM HOT-TODDY?

NOT JUST YET, MR. BURNS, BUT CAPT. SLAMTASTIC IS HERE TO SEE YOU.

BLAST! ANOTHER BANANA REPUBLIC MILITIA MAN HERE BEGGING ME TO FUND SOME SORT OF TERRITORIAL SQUABBLE?

ACTUALLY, SIR, HE'S A PROFESSIONAL WRESTLER. IF YOU RECALL, ONE OF YOUR TAX SHELTERS IS SPONSORING SEVERAL STRONG MEN IN THE UNIVERSAL WRESTLING ASSOCIATION.

PLEASE, IF YOU'LL JUST LET ME GET TO MY CHECKBOOK, I'M SURE WE CAN COME TO AN ARRANGEMENT.

HAVE YOU HAD ENOUGH, SMITHERS?

PLEASE, SIR, PUT ME IN A FULL-NELSON AGAIN.

DID I EVER REGALE YOU WITH STORIES OF MY WRESTLING PROWESS, SMITHERS?

INSPIRING STORIES--EVERY ONE OF THEM, SIR.

WELL, BY ALL MEANS, STOP DAYDREAMING AND SEND ADMIRAL WHATSHISNAME IN.

YES, SIR.

YOU'VE HAD QUITE A CAREER, CAPTAIN *SPAM*TASTIC. TO WHAT DO YOU ATTRIBUTE YOUR UNFLAGGING SUCCESS?

YOU KNOW, MR. BURNS... THE FACT THAT ALL THE FIGHTS ARE *FIXED*.

THEY'RE *WHAT!?!* THIS IS AN *OUTRAGE!* WHO IS THE TWO-BIT SHILL WHO WOULD *PERPETRATE* THIS KIND OF SHAM?

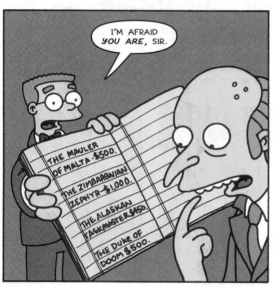

I'M AFRAID *YOU ARE*, SIR.

THE MAULER OF MALTA-$500.

THE ZIMBARBVIAN ZEPHYR-$1,000.

THE ALASKAN TASKMASTER-$450.

THE DUKE OF DOOM-$500.

YOU SEE, BY INSURING CAPTAIN SLAMTASTIC'S SUCCESS IN THE RING, WE INCREASE THE POPULARITY OF HIS MERCHANDISE. THIS BRINGS IN APPROXIMATELY 3.2 MILLION A YEAR AND CHANGE *AND* IS OWNED BY *BURNS, INC.*

CAPT. SLAMTASTIC VS. Pharmacist Phil "SAY NO TO DRUGS"

EXCELLENT, SMITHERS, *EXCELLENT!* BUT WHY DIDN'T I *KNOW* ABOUT THIS?

AS I SAID, SIR, IT *ONLY* BRINGS IN 3.2 MILLION A YEAR AND CHANGE. I DIDN'T WANT TO BOTHER YOU WITH AN INVESTMENT THAT SMALL.

SO, MY GOOD CAPTAIN, WHAT BRINGS *YOU* HERE? HAVE YOU COME TO IMPART GRATIS TO THE HAND THAT FEEDS OR BEG FOR A LARGER PERCENTAGE OF THE PALTRY SUM I MAKE FROM YOUR LIKENESS?

WELL, MR. BURNS, I'VE COME TO LET YOU KNOW I PLAN TO ANNOUNCE MY RETIREMENT.

AS OF THIS MOMENT I'M SAYING, *"GOOD-BYE!,"* TO CAPTAIN SLAMTASTIC, UWA CHAMPION AND, *"WELCOME BACK,"* TO THE REAL ME, *GARY SALTZMAN, PTA CHAIRMAN.*

LATER...

MY FELLOW, AH, FISH FANCIERS--IN A TRADITION THAT IS AS SYMBIOTIC TO POLITICS AS IT IS TO, AH, WRESTLING...

OOOH, I HAD TOO MUCH GROG. I'D BETTER RUN TO THE HEAD. ⌐HEH-HEH⌐ I LOVE SHIP LINGO.

IF ONLY I WEREN'T ALLERGIC TO THIS DACRON UNITARD. I HAVE A FEELING I WOULD BE BETTER OFF DONNING THIS OUTFIT MYSELF.

...WE WILL NOW COMMENCE WITH THE PRE-CONTEST *NAME CALLING* AND, ER, *MUD-SLINGING*.

EXCUSE ME, MR. SIMPSON. MIGHT I INTEREST YOU IN A LITTLE PROPOSITION?

FIRST MATES

PROPOSITION? *PROPOSITION*? I'M SICK OF YOUR LOUSY PROPOSITIONS! ILLEGAL ALIENS, NO FAULT INSURANCE, CATS ON DRUGS-- WHO CARES?

LISTEN, SIMPSON, I'VE BEEN AUTHORIZED TO, AH, *DOUBLE* YOUR SALARY AND THEN, AH, DIVIDE IT BY *TWO* AND PAY YOU AN EXTRA *THREE DOLLARS A MONTH* ON TOP OF THAT. ALL YOU HAVE TO DO IS PUT *THIS* ON AND SIGN *THIS*.

ALL I HAVE TO DO IS PUT ON THIS THING THAT LOOKS LIKE CAPTAIN SLAMTASTIC'S COSTUME, AND YOU'LL DO ALL THAT MATH TO MY SALARY?

LET'S SEE, WHAT WAS THAT THING MARGE ALWAYS SAYS? OH, YEAH, "IF IT SOUNDS TOO GOOD TO BE TRUE, IT PROBABLY IS." HMMM, BUT SHE ALSO SAYS, "DON'T LOOK A GIFT HORSE IN THE MOUTH."

FIRST MATES

SO, LET'S SEE IS THIS A *"HORSE THING"* OR A *"GOOD THING"*...EENY, MEENY, MINEY --

OH ALRIGHT, IT ONLY COMES OUT TO A *$36 A YEAR RAISE!*

WOO HOO! HELLO, UPPER-LOWER-MIDDLE CLASS!

43

IN A MOMENT...

I SWEAR TO ZION, MON, THAT I WILL MERCILESSLY PLACE MY OPPRESSOR, CAPTAIN SLAMTASTIC, IN A *"NATTY DREADLOCK"* HEADLOCK. I-RE-I!

EASY SKANKING, DUDE! WHATEVER *THAT* MEANS.

GOOD MORROW, MY FINE FRIENDS. LET IT BEKNOWNST THAT I SHALL LAND UPON THE CAPTAIN, MUCH AS MY FOREFATHERS LANDED ON PLYMOUTH ROCK. HOWEVER, THERE SHALL BE VERY LITTLE LEFT OF HIM FOR TOURISTS TO VISIT AT THANKSGIVING.

I'M NOT SURE HIS IMAGE WOULD SIT WELL WITH 'OL *MILES STANDISH*, BUT HIS PURITANICAL SPIRIT SURE GIVES ME SOMETHING TO ROOTILY-TOOT FOR.

YOU DID SAY THAT THE *REAL* CAPTAIN SLAMTASTIC WAS GOING TO BE HERE FOR THE BONE-CRUSHING, BACK-SPRAINING, FIGHTING PART, RIGHT?

YOU'VE GOT NOTHING TO WORRY ABOUT, MR. SIMPSON.

AND NOW THE MOMENT YOU'VE ALL BEEN WAITING FOR--ALLOW ME TO, AH, INTRODUCE THAT HAVOC-WREAKING, RIB-SNAPPING, TIBIA-TWISTING, UNIVERSAL WRESTLING ASSOCIATION CHAMPION, *CAPTAIN SLAMTASTIC!!*

I FEEL KINDA SILLY IN THIS OUTFIT--GOOD THING MY FAMILY CAN'T SEE ME.

MEANWHILE AT PATTY AND SELMA'S...

NOW, ISN'T IT NICE TO HAVE A FAMILY MEAL WITHOUT THAT PRIMATE HUSBAND OF YOURS?

THOSE CHEWING NOISES HE MAKES ARE JUST LIKE THE SOUNDS THE DISHWASHER MAKES WHEN MY GIRDLE CAUSES THE RINSE CYCLE TO JAM.

YOU KNOW, SUDDENLY, I'M NOT ALL THAT HUNGRY.

NOW, I HOPE YOU KIDS DON'T MIND, BUT WE THOUGHT, INSTEAD OF SUFFERING THROUGH INANE DINNER CONVERSATION ABOUT OUR DAILY ROUTINES OR MILDLY AMUSING ANECDOTES OF YOUR EXPLOITS AT SCHOOL, WE'D ALL SIT BACK AND WATCH A LITTLE TV.

I'LL AGREE TO ANYTHING THAT KEEPS THEM FROM BAD-MOUTHING HOMEY IN FRONT OF THE KIDS. I HOPE HE'S OKAY.

MEANWHILE...

HELLO, UH, I'M HERE TO, UH...

KICK SOME BUTT!

THAT'S RIGHT! TO, AH, KICK SOME BUTT!

CLAP CLAP CLAP CLAP CLAP CLAP

OH, YEAH! THAT WAS EASY. CAN I GET CHANGED NOW? I WANT TO PUT MY FAT PANTS BACK ON.

NOT JUST YET. THERE'S JUST ONE OTHER THING I NEED YOU TO DO FOR ME.

THAT NIGHT IN THE SIMPSON KITCHEN...

...AND I KNOW YOU HAVEN'T HEARD FROM ME IN A LONG TIME, LORD, BUT I TRULY MUST THANK YOU FOR SHOWING MOM THE LIGHT OF THE ALL-NITE KRUSTY BURGER'S NEON SIGN SO THAT WE MIGHT EAT A DECENT MEAL.

AMEN, BROTHER!

HOMER, WHERE HAVE YOU BEEN? YOU WERE SUPPOSED TO HAVE BEEN HERE BY YOURSELF, THINKING ABOUT THE ERROR OF YOUR WAYS.

MARGE, USUALLY I'D TRY TO MAKE UP AN ELABORATE STORY THAT YOU WOULD NEVER, EVER BELIEVE.

BUT I HAVE LEARNED THAT HONESTY IS THE BEST POLICY. THE TRUTH IS THAT I HAVE A NEW SECRET IDENTITY AS A PROFESSIONAL WRESTLER.

HOMER J. SIMPSON, THAT IS THE MOST COCKAMAMIE STORY I'VE HEARD YOU TELL YET!

EVEN WORSE THAN THE TIME HOMER TRIED TO TELL YOU THAT HE WENT TO A FOOTBALL GAME ON YOUR ANNIVERSARY BECAUSE HE LEFT YOUR PRESENT AT THE STADIUM?

OR THE TIME HE TRIED TO CONVINCE YOU THAT THE LAWN GROWS BETTER IF YOU ONLY MOW IT ONCE A MONTH?

THE DIFFERENCE IS THAT *THIS* COCKAMAMIE STORY IS *TRUE*!

HA HA HA

SO'S *THIS* ONE. I'M GOING UPSTAIRS TO DO MY *HOMEWORK*.

HA HA HA HA HA

VERY FUNNY. NOW, IF YOU'LL *EXCUSE* ME, I HAVE TO REST UP FOR MY MATCH TOMORROW.

HO, HO TEE-HEE HOO, HA HA

LATER...

IT SEEMS AS IF CAPTAIN SLAMTASTIC HAS BEATEN ALL THE BADDEST OF THE BAD BOYS IN THE UWA.

THAT'S RIGHT, MARTY, AND HE'S QUICKLY BECOME ONE OF THE MOST POPULAR SPORTS FIGURES IN SPRINGFIELD.

HOMER, I GOTTA TELL YA, I HEAR A LOT OF BULL FLYIN' AROUND THIS BAR, BUT THAT *TAKES* IT. HEH, HEH, YOU...*A PROFESSIONAL WRESTLER?!?*

FIRST, YOU TELL US YOU'RE A SAFETY INSPECTOR AT THE POWER PLANT AND NOW THIS! WHAT KIND OF IDIOTS DO YOU TAKES US FOR?

:BUUURRRP!:

I'M TELLING YOU, THAT'S *ME!*

DRINK Duff.

THAT AIN'T YOU, HOMER, THAT'S CAPTAIN SLAMTASTIC.

THAT'S WHAT I'M TRYING TO TELL YOU, I'M CAPTAIN-- *HEY!*

SORRY, HOMER, BUT YOU'VE OBVIOUSLY HAD TOO MUCH TO DRINK. YOU'RE GETTIN' DELUSIONAL.

WALL OF FAME

FINE, MOE. DON'T COME RUNNING TO ME FOR A CELEBRITY ENDORSEMENT WHEN *I'M* RICH AND FAMOUS.

AND WITH HIS POPULARITY SOARING, THE SLAMTASTIC MERCHANDISING TRAIN IS HEADED TOWARDS *YOU* WITH A FULL HEAD OF STEAM!

THE NEXT DAY...

YOU'VE GOTTA HELP ME, BARNEY. I CAN'T LET MR. BURNS DOWN--HE ACTUALLY BELIEVES IN ME.

HOMER, HOW CAN I, YOUR FRIEND, CONTRIBUTE IN GOOD CONSCIENCE TO YOUR DELUSION OF BEING CAPTAIN SLAMTASTIC?

I Drink, THEREFORE I'm Drunk

DEAL! C'MON HOMER, WE'VE GOT A LOT OF WORK TO DO!

I'LL PAY YOU IN DUFF.

THE JAWBREAKER

El Barto

WAIT--AREN'T WE SUPPOSED TO BE TRAINING?

DOGS

OH, YEAH. C'MON HOMER! WE'VE GOT A LOT OF WORK TO DO...

A WEEK LATER, INSIDE THE SPRINGFIELD SPORTS FORUM...

LET'S GET READY TO...*GRAPPLE*!!!

YOU CAN DO IT, HOMER, JUST LIKE WE TRAINED ALL WEEK--ONLY HE ISN'T GOING TO JUST SIT THERE DRINKING BEER AND EATING PRETZELS.

REMEMBER, TRY NOT TO HURT THE FELLOW, BUT MAKE IT LOOK *REAL*! WE DON'T WANT ANOTHER "TYSON-SELDON" FIASCO ON OUR HANDS.

DON'T WORRY, MR. BURNS. I COULD HAVE LOST TO *DUKAKIS IN '88* AND MADE IT LOOK REAL.

DING, DING!

AND THE BATTLE BEGINS!

I TOLD YOU THE MAN'S A PRO, SIR.

UNFORTUNATELY FOR YOU, MR. BIG BAD SCARY WRESTLING *CHALLENGER*, I'M THE *NEW AND IMPROVED* CAPTAIN SLAMTASTIC!

OH, FOR CRYING OUT LOUD, ENOUGH OF THE FALSE BRAVADO. LET'S JUST START THIS CHARADE, SHALL WE?

THE END

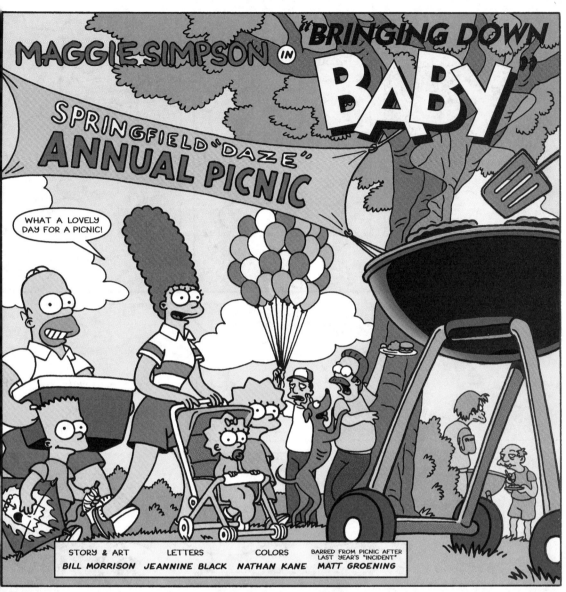

MAGGIE SIMPSON IN "BRINGING DOWN BABY"

SPRINGFIELD "DAZE" ANNUAL PICNIC

WHAT A LOVELY DAY FOR A PICNIC!

STORY & ART	LETTERS	COLORS	BARRED FROM PICNIC AFTER LAST YEAR'S "INCIDENT"
BILL MORRISON	JEANNINE BLACK	NATHAN KANE	MATT GROENING

THIS LOOKS LIKE A GOOD SPOT.

HERE, MAGGIE, YOU PLAY WITH YOUR RATTLE WHILE I FIX YOU A JAR OF "BABY'S FIRST PICNIC FOOD."

PFFFT!

I THINK WE'LL TRY THE PURÉED CHILI DOG.

THE END

OTTO'S Top 40

1. Garfield
2. The First Amendment

3. Big ol' gnarly tattoos of flaming skulls
4. "Stairway to Heaven"
5. Extra-spicy hickory-smoked beef jerky
6. Erik von Däniken's *Chariots of the Gods*
7. Festival seating
8. Susan Dey
9. Baby humans that have been raised by wolves.
10. The cool way a busload of kids eating corn nuts smells
11. Super-long, intense guitar riffs played with a wah-wah pedal
12. Bandanas on dogs
13. Tape hiss
14. Totally spacing out and forgetting where the bus is parked

15. Space-age neo-psychedelic head-banger music
16. Grinding all four gears going up a killer incline
17. 20-minute drum solos
18. Bizarre conspiracy theories involving the military and U.F.O.'s
19. Foam rubber
20. Letting your freak flag fly
21. Giving the thumbs-up sign to other bus drivers
22. Politically disenfranchised white male suburban hell-raisers
23. The Miranda Decision
24. 42" woofers
25. Poems about the universe
26. Slowing down to rubber-neck some roadside disaster
27. Pinball
28. Vinyl records
29. Double-dipped, deep-fat-fried corn dogs
30. Underground comix
31. That totally intense look you get on your face when you're playing "Wrathchild" on air guitar
32. Passive-aggressive babes of the female persuassion
33. Buzz Cola with twice the sugar, twice the caffeine
34. Air fresheners shaped like trees that really smell like trees
35. Mood rings
36. Onion rings
37. The mesh thing you put on the seat that keeps your butt from getting clammy
38. Finding an unopened bag of Chee-tos under a bus seat
39. Chain-link fencing
40. "Inna Gadda Da Vida"

SMITHERSES!

SCRIPT
DAN STUDNEY
& JIM LINCOLN

PENCILS
STEPHANIE GLADDEN &
BILL MORRISON (PGS. 15-17)

INKS
TIM BAVINGTON &
TIM HARKINS (PGS. 12-14)

LETTERS
JEANNINE BLACK

COLORS
NATHAN KANE

THE CLONE
RANGER
MATT GROENING

THOSE *STRIKING WORKERS* HAVE BECOME QUITE A BOIL ON MY BACKSIDE, SMITHERS. THE TIME HAS COME FOR *DRASTIC ACTION*.

DRASTIC ACTION, SIR? YOU DON'T MEAN...

YES. AFTER WEEKS OF BULLHEADED NEGO-TIATION AND POLITICAL MANEUVERING, PERHAPS IT'S TIME TO ACTUALLY *FIND OUT WHAT IT IS THEY WANT*.

POOF!

WORKER DEMANDS

THEY'RE HOLDING OUT FOR A FIVE CENT WAGE INCREASE.

WORKER DEMANDS

FIVE PERCENT!?

NO, *FIVE CENTS*, SIR. A *NICKEL*.

NEVER! THEY WON'T SQUEEZE ONE HAYPENNY OUT OF ME!

5¢ INCREASE

THEY WANT TO PLAY HARDBALL, EH? WELL, WE'LL JUST SEE HOW BADLY THEY WANT THEIR PRECIOUS FIVE CENTS WHEN THEY HAVE *NO POWER!*

OVER THE NEXT FEW WEEKS...

...AND SO THE QUESTION ON EVERYONE'S MIND IS: IS THIS INTENTIONAL POWER OUTAGE SIMPLY A *NEGOTIATION TACTIC* OR IS IT THE *BRUTAL RETALIATION* OF A BITTER OLD MAN? EITHER WAY, THIS REPORTER IS STILL IN THE DARK. I'M KENT BROCKMAN...

...AND THAT'S THE NEWS. NOW, I'M OFF TO THE FLANDERS' HOUSE.

HEY, HOW COME AUNT PATTY AND AUNT SELMA HAVE LIGHTS?

THE POWER IS OUT AND THIS MEAT IS THREE WEEKS PAST IT'S PRIME.

TIME TO LABEL IT *JERKY!*

67

LATER, AT MR. BURNS' PRIVATE LAB...

WHAT'S *THIS*, SMITHERS? I THOUGHT WE WERE HERE TO LEARN ABOUT *CLONING*.

WE ARE, SIR. THIS THEATER TRAVELS FROM ROOM TO ROOM, TAKING US ON AN AUTOMATED TOUR OF THE LAB THAT WILL EXPLAIN HOW THE PROCESS WORKS.

OH, GOODIE, A *SHOW!* MAYHAP IT WILL BE A CAUTIONARY TALE OF TECHNOLOGY GONE *AWRY* WITH SPECTACULAR SPECIAL EFFECTS AND PAPER THIN CHARACTERS.

NO, SIR. IT WAS MADE FOR *US*, NOT THE *AMERICAN PUBLIC*.

HOWDY! SMILIN' JOE FISSION HERE, AND I'M GONNA TELL YOU ALL ABOUT *CLONING!*

WE'VE COMBINED *DNA GENETICS* AND *NUCLEAR TECHNOLOGY* TO CREATE THE MUTATED ABOMINATION KNOWN AS *A CLONE!*

Gregor Mendel

FROM A SINGLE DROP OF BLOOD, OUR SCIENTISTS CAN CREATE AN IDENTICAL BEING.

NOW, IF YOU'LL REMOVE THE RADIATION-PROOF PONCHOS FROM UNDERNEATH YOUR SEATS, WE'LL TAKE YOU INTO THE LAB WHERE THE LI'L FELLERS HATCH.

BAM! BAM!

WHIRRR!

I ALWAYS LIKE TO *BE* HERE WHEN EACH LITTLE BUNDLE OF GENETIC JOY IS *BORN!* ⋲WHOO-HEY⋺

THIS IS *IT*, SMITHERS. I CERTAINLY HOPE OUR LITTLE MOPPET HERE DOESN'T DISAPPOINT.

I DO TOO, SIR.

BURNS LABS
Employees must wash hands after exposure to radioactive core.

CRACKKK

POP!

MEANWHILE, BACK AT THE POWER PLANT...

THIS IS WORKING OUT *SPLENDIDLY*, SMITHERS.

PRODUCTIVITY IS UP, PROFITS ARE *SOARING*, AND MOST IMPORTANTLY, SLAVISH DEVOTION AND SYCOPHANTIC WORSHIP ARE ABSOLUTELY *THROUGH THE ROOF!*

I'VE NEVER BEEN HAPPIER.

WE'D BETTER GET MOVING, SIR. IT'S ALMOST TIME FOR YOUR MASSAGE.

AH, YES. I HOPE YOUR FINGERNAILS ARE PROPERLY CLIPPED. LAST TIME YOU LEFT GHASTLY SCRATCHES DOWN MY BACK.

SLAM!

I SAW WHAT YOU WERE DOING. YOU WERE *DELIBERATELY* TRYING TO MAKE ME LOOK BAD IN FRONT OF *MONTY*.

THAT'S *MR. BURNS* TO *YOU!*

BIFF!

POW!

TAKE IT EASY, 73. YOU'RE HURTING HIM.

THAT'S IT, STICK TOGETHER. YOU *EVEN* NUMBERS ALL THINK YOU'RE *SOOO* GREAT!

LATER...

WELL, IT SEEMS OUR IDENTICAL LITTLE FRIENDS ARE HAVING SOME SLIGHT *ADJUSTMENT* PROBLEMS.

I'D SAY SO, SIR. SEVENTEEN CLONES DEAD TO DATE, THREE NEAR MELTDOWNS AND SEVERE STRUCTURAL DAMAGE TO SECTOR 7-G.

AND PLANT EFFICIENCY?

STILL 58% HIGHER THAN WITH THE REGULAR WORKERS.

I REALLY DON'T THINK IT'S SAFE FOR YOU TO BE OUT HERE, SIR.

OH, *POPPYCOCK*. I LOVE WALKING AMIDST ALL MY *LOYAL SUBJECTS*.

PLEASE, SIR. MAY I HAVE AN AUTOGRAPH? IT'S, UM... FOR MY MOTHER.

YOUR MOTHER'S A *TEST TUBE*! NOW LEAVE MR. BURNS ALONE!

THAT GOES FOR *ALL* OF YOU!

WHONK!

MR. BURNS THREW IT AWAY IN *MY* GARBAGE CAN!

BUT *I'M* IN CHARGE OF ALL *SANITATION*. THE SOILED TISSUE IS RIGHTFULLY *MINE*!

BROTHERS, *PLEASE*! WE'RE READY TO KILL EACH OTHER OVER A FEW *MUCOUS-LADEN SCRAPS*!

ALL WE REALLY NEED IS TOTAL ACCESS TO MR. BURNS, AND THERE'S ONLY *ONE* MAN DENYING IT. WE *MUST* GET RID OF THE ORIGINAL. WE MUST...

...KILL SMITHERS PRIME!

ELSEWHERE IN THE POWER PLANT...

COULD YOU TELL ME HOW TO GET TO THE CLONING LAB, PLEASE?

WHY SHOULD I TELL *YOU*?

I ONCE SAVED MR. BURNS' LIFE BY DONATING BLOOD.

YOU ARE A *GOD*! DOWN THE HALL, THIRD DOOR ON THE LEFT.

MAN, THOSE SMITHERS CLONES ARE CREEPY. AND THERE'S SO MANY OF THEM. I WONDER HOW YOU TELL WHO THE *REAL* ONE IS...

HELP, HELP! THEY'RE GOING TO KILL ME IN A HORRIBLE, VICIOUS...

IS THAT THE SIMPSON BOY?

...NASTY, VIOLENT WAY! *HELP, HELP!*

DON'T PANIC. REMAIN CALM. AS LONG AS THEY DON'T KNOW I'M HERE I'LL BE SAFE.

BESIDES, MR. BURNS IS MONITORING EVERYTHING. *HE'LL* SAVE ME.

THIS THRICE-CURSED CUTICLE IS DRIVING ME MAD. I NEED A BUFF AND I NEED IT *NOW!* WHERE IS SMITHERS AND HIS DANCING EMERY BOARD?

AH, *THERE* YOU ARE, HIDDEN IN SHADOW BEHIND THE PARTICLE ACCELERATOR. COME HERE, SMITHERS. I NEED YOU.

AFTER HIM!!

ARE YOU SURE THIS PLAN IS GOING TO WORK?

DON'T WORRY. JUST SIT BACK AND LET *LLEWELLYN SINCLAIR* WORK HIS *MAGIC*.

A *WIG*, A TOUCH OF MAKE-UP *HERE*, A HUGE TUMMY-TUCK DOWN *THERE*, AND I THINK WE *MAY* HAVE A *WINNER!*

EIGHT HOURS LATER...

I'VE *OUTDONE* MYSELF THIS TIME!

WHAT DO YOU THINK, HOMER?

I LOOK LIKE MR. BURNS.

THAT *IS* WHO I'M SUPPOSED TO LOOK LIKE, ISN'T IT?

LATER, AT THE POWER PLANT...

STAY IN CHARACTER, HOMER. THINK MEAN, GREEDY THOUGHTS.

MR. BURNS! HOW DID YOU GET OUTSIDE WITHOUT ONE OF OUR SPECIALLY-ASSIGNED SURVEILLANCE CLONES KNOWING ABOUT IT?

HE CAME OUT TO BRING ME BACK! NOW, *STEP ASIDE!*

IT WORKED, HOMER. IF WE CAN FOOL *THAT* ONE, WE CAN FOOL THEM *ALL!*

NOW ALL WE HAVE TO DO IS FIND BART AND MONTY AND WE CAN WALTZ RIGHT OUT OF HERE.

WELCOME TO WORK SMITHERSES

TSK, TSK. NOT ONE DONUT TAKEN. THOSE CLONES MAY BE SMART ENOUGH TO TAKE OVER AND RUN A NUCLEAR POWER PLANT...

...BUT THEY'RE TOO STUPID TO KNOW THE MOUTH-WATERING JOY THAT IS A *DELUXE PINK FROSTED CRULLER!*

HOMER, *NO!* YOU'RE EATING YOUR PROSTHETIC MAKE-UP!

MMMM ¦GLOMPH¦ MMMM-- OW!

¦GASP!¦ *LOOK EVERYONE*--A WOLF IN BURNS' CLOTHING! A FAT WOLF!

GET 'EM!

LATER... PEOPLE OF SPRINGFIELD, THE SITUATION IS *CRITICAL*. HELP MR. BURNS IN HIS TIME OF NEED AND YOU WILL BE *REWARDED!*

WHERE WAS HE IN OUR TIME OF NEED? HE TURNED HIS BACK ON HIS WORKERS AND RUINED THE WHOLE TOWN!

YEAH! HE SHOWED US THE DOOR AND HIRED MUTANT SLAVES!

AND SPRINGFIELD'S LACK OF DISPOSABLE INCOME HAS CAUSED MY PROFITS TO MELT AWAY LIKE A *CHERRY SQUISHEE* IN THE BOWELS OF *HELL*, SIR!

IT'S NOT JUST MR. BURNS THAT'S IN TROUBLE. THERE'S A *LOST CHILD* SOMEWHERE IN THAT POWER PLANT. HE'S COLD AND FRIGHTENED AND NEEDS YOU ALL TO *SAVE* HIM!

IF THERE'S A CHILD IN DANGER, I *MUST* HELP. I CAN WHIP A RAG-TAG GROUP INTO A PRECISE FIGHTING CORPS IN A MATTER OF HOURS. WHO *IS* THIS POOR, HELPLESS YOUTH?

MY SON, BART. ALSO KNOWN AS "THE BOY."

WELL, THAT'S A DIFFERENT MATTER ENTIRELY.

DRINKS ARE ON ME!

WE'RE *STAYIN'* TILL THE ALE'S DRUNK DOWN TO THE *BITTER DREGS!*

SORRY, THE KEG'S TAPPED OUT.

OH. IN THAT CASE, WHAT SAY WE HELP OUT THE OLD MISER?

AND...?

:SIGH: *AND* THE DELINQUENT. ALL IN FAVOR?

AYE-DIDDLY-DO.

:URRRRRUP:

78

81

WELL, I GOT THEM CHASING ME. NOW WHAT DO I DO?

KEEP RUNNING!

MR. BURNS, I NEED YOUR HELP!

SORRY, LAD, BUT I'M A TIDGE BUSY RIGHT NOW BEING DISMEMBERED BY HOMICIDAL CLONES!

OWIE! DON'T YANK ON *THAT*! IT'S *ATTACHED*!

DID MY EYES DECEIVE ME OR WAS THAT A BICENTENNIAL STACEY?

STARS AND GARTERS, *I'VE GOTTA HAVE IT.*

IT'S FUNNY. I'M PLEASED TO BE ALIVE AND IN ONE PIECE, YET I SOMEHOW MISS THEIR GENTLE BONHOMIE.

BART, HURRY! INSIDE!

HOW'D YOU GET HERE AHEAD OF ME AND THE CLONES?

THEY MAY HAVE MY GENETIC MAKE-UP AND MY MEMORY, BUT THEY DON'T HAVE MY INGENUITY. I CAN GET FROM ANY SECTION OF THIS PLANT TO MR. BURNS' OFFICE IN TWENTY SECONDS OR LESS.

NOW, IT'S TIME FOR ME TO TAKE IT FROM HERE.

LATER...

WELL DONE, SMITHERS. YOU DID AN *EXCELLENT* JOB OF QUELLING THE UNRULY HOARD OF MONSTROSITIES AND SAVING MY LIFE.

I DID HAVE SOME HELP, SIR. ALL THESE BRAVE EX-EMPLOYEES AND TOWNSPEOPLE...

...WHO WERE WILLING TO RISK THEIR LIVES FOR YOU AT A MOMENT'S NOTICE WITHOUT ANY REGARD FOR THEIR OWN PERSONAL SAFETY.

AND WITH NO THOUGHT OF REWARD.

NO THOUGHT OF *REWARD*, EH? HOW *LUCKY FOR US*.

WHAT ARE WE GOING TO DO WITH THE CLONES?

PERHAPS WE SHOULD KILL THEM.

YES, *THAT'S* IT. EVERYONE GRAB A FIREARM. IT'LL BE LIKE SHOOTING FISH IN A BARREL.

JUST A MINUTE, SIR. IS IT REALLY *NECESSARY* TO KILL THEM *ALL*? I MEAN, THEY *ARE* FLESH OF MY FLESH, SO TO SPEAK.

WHY SHOULD WE SPARE THEIR LIVES, SMITHERS? WHAT HAVE THEY GIVEN US APART FROM A COMPELLING STORY WITH THE CLASSIC ELEMENTS OF OBSESSION, JEALOUSY, BETRAYAL AND DERRING-DO!

AND PERHAPS, A LITTLE SINGING AND DANCING.

WHAT CAN WE POSSIBLY DO WITH *THAT*?

WE'LL SET IT TO *MUSIC* AND TAKE IT TO *BROADWAY!*

BART & MILHOUSE IN "BORE US THE MOVIE GRUEL"

SCRIPT	PENCILS	INKS	LETTERS	COLORS	MULE DIALECT COACH
ROB WALTON	PHIL ORTIZ	TIM BAVINGTON	JEANNINE BLACK	NATHAN KANE	MATT GROENING

SAY, GANG, WE NEED ONE MORE GUY FOR THE BIG DANCE TONIGHT. HOW ABOUT *PETER LEWIS* OVER THERE?

ARE YOU KIDDING? THAT *NUCLEAH NERD* WOULDN'T KNOW A CHA-CHA FROM A WALTZ.

PETER LEWIS? *HIS* IDEA OF A *PIN-UP GIRL* IS A PICTURE OF THE *ENOLA GAY!*

JEEPERS! THEY THINK I'M A SQUARE JUST BECAUSE I LIKE *SCIENCE.* MAYBE IF I SHOW GWEN HOW *IMPORTANT* SCIENCE CAN BE, SHE'LL SEE HOW *SWELL* I AM.

WHY WOULD YOU NEED ONE MORE GUY FOR A DANCE?

I'D LOVE TO COME TO THE DANCE TONIGHT, BUT I'VE GOT AN IMPORTANT PAPER TO PREPARE ON THE *H-BOMB.* I'VE BEEN INVITED BY *EDWARD TELLER* TO *LOS ALAMOS* THIS SUMMER.

:HUMPH!:

:SNIFF, SNIFF: :SOB!:

BUT I WHA-HA-HA-HANTED SPACE MUTANTS!

PULL IT TOGETHER, MILHOUSE! WE PAID OUR *NON-REFUNDABLE ADMISSION* SO WE MAY AS WELL MAKE THE *BEST* OF IT.

I MUST RETIAH AS WELL. DA BIG GAME AGAINST NOTRE DAME IS TOMORROW. AND *I'VE* BEEN INVITED BY *VINCE LOMBARDI* TO TRY OUT FOR DA *GREEN BAY PACKERS* DIS SUMMER.

OH, BASH, THAT'S SO EXCITING! EVERYONE KNOWS THE *REAL* MONEY LIES IN PROFESSIONAL SPORTS, *NOT* THE MILITARY INDUSTRIAL COMPLEX.

HA HA HA

SMEK!

HOW AM I EVER GOING TO COMPETE WITH JOCKS LIKE *BASH FLASHMAN?* UNLESS...

HEADS UP, BASH!

THAT'S *IT!* ALL I HAVE TO DO IS JOIN THE *FOOTBALL TEAM* AND BE THE *HERO* OF THE BIG GAME TOMORROW! I'LL TALK TO COACH RIGHT AWAY!

OH NO, SOMEBODY FORGOT TO TELL HIM HE'S A *NUCLEAH NERD!*

REALLY, COACH. I WANT TO PLAY IN THE BIG GAME TOMORROW.

HA-HA-HA-HA-HA! STOP IT, KID! YER *KILLIN'* ME!

:KAK!:

SERIOUSLY! I THINK I SWALLOWED MY *WHISTLE...*

COACH

I THINK YOU SWALLOWED *DETROIT!*

LISTEN, BRAINIAC, NOW THAT YOU MENTION IT, THERE *IS* A SPOT ON THE TEAM FOR A YOUNG GO-GETTER WITH YER KINDA BOOK SMARTS.

BRAINIAC, HAH! THAT'S A *GOOD* ONE, HUH, BART?

COACH

YEAH, YEAH, GIMME SOME MORE SPACE MUTANT-JUBES.

A LITTLE.

BUT MOSTLY I FEEL *CHEATED* BECAUSE I DIDN'T GET TO DRESS UP AS A *YUMMY TART!* IT WOULD HAVE BEEN THE PERFECT COSTUME...

...SATISFYING MY NEED TO WIN *AND* MY PHYSICAL ADDICTION TO TASTY SNACK TREATS!

BEST COSTUME

WELL, I HAVE NEEDS TOO, YOU KNOW, AND ONE OF THEM INVOLVES SLOW DANCING WITH THE MAN I LOVE, *WITHOUT* THE FEAR OF BEING COVERED IN STICKY FRUIT FILLING.

WELL, IF WE HAD TO DRESS AS A COUPLE, WHY DIDN'T YOU RENT SOMETHING A LITTLE LESS REVEALING?

A MAN HAS TO HAVE *SOME* SECRETS Y'KNOW!

SECRETS? BELIEVE ME HOMER, BETWEEN THE *STREAKING* IN THE 70'S, AND THE *MOONING* IN THE 80'S AND :SIGH: THE 90'S, YOU *HAVE* NO SECRETS!

BESIDES, HELEN LOVEJOY BEAT ME TO THE STAR WARS COSTUMES, AND THIS WAS ALL THE MASQUERADE SHOP HAD LEFT.

YOUR ATTENTION PLEASE, REGISTERED VOTERS. KINDLY DIRECT YOUR ATTENTION TO THE BANDSTAND WHERE YOUR BELOVED MAYOR, *DIAMOND JOE QUIMBY* WILL NOW AWARD THE PRIZE FOR *BEST COSTUME!*

SNAP! CRACKLE! POP!

OOH, COME ON, HOMER! YOU COULD STILL WIN!

YEAH, FAT CHANCE IN *THIS* STUPID GET-UP.

AND THE, AH, AWARD GOES TO...

...THIS *YUMMY LITTLE TART!*

THE LARRY DAVIS EXPERIEN

D'OH!

MY DEAR, PLEASE ACCEPT THIS ER, AH, SYMBOLIC KEY TO THE CITY...

...ALONG WITH THE KEY TO MY SUITE AT THE *"WHO'S TO KNOW MOTEL!"*

YEA!

WHOOPEE!

YEA!

THANKS A *LOT* MARGE! THAT COULD HAVE BEEN *ME!*

=SIGH=

THE LARRY DAVIS

YOU'D BETTER JUST WATCH YOUR STEP, QUIMBY! THAT'S *MY* WOMAN YOU'RE MESSING WITH! A DIVORCE IS JUST A PIECE OF PAPER! THE SECRET MARRIAGE IS NEVER BROKEN!

REMEMBER, THE HILLS HAVE EYES, QUIMBY!

THE HILLS HAVE EYES!!

EXCUSE ME, MARGE, BUT THANKS TO *YOU* I'VE STILL GOT A PHYSICAL ADDICTION TO SATISFY.

IF YOU NEED ME, I'LL BE AT THE REFRESHMENT TABLE.

MMM...MAYOR QUIMBY LAID OUT QUITE A SPREAD THIS YEAR. COCKTAIL WEENIES... AEROSOL CHEESE...*SMACK*... PORK RINDS...AND PLENTY OF KETCHUP FOR DIPPING!

CITY TREASURY
BUDGET SHORTFALL FUND-RAISER
ADMISSION $35
(Non-Tax-Deductible)

This event is fully staffed by Springfield city employees on overtime. Your tax dollars hard at work!

HUNDREDS OF DOLLARS...AND IT'S *MINE! ALL MINE!*

BAH! THIS WAS TOO EASY...A *WASTE* OF THE SUPREME GENIUS OF *DR. COLOSSUS!*

EXIT

EEP! PERHAPS I SPOKE TOO SOON. *CHIEF WIGGUM* HAS CLEVERLY SEALED MY ESCAPE ROUTE.

I WILL HAVE TO EXIT THROUGH THE GYMNASIUM. BUT SINCE THIS IS A MASQUERADE BALL, I WILL BLEND IN *PERFECTLY!* NONE WILL SUSPECT THAT I, THE *PHYSICIAN OF FELONIOUSNESS,* AM IN THEIR MIDST!

CRUNCH!

THAT SHOULD BE ENOUGH FOR NOW.

HELLO, MR. BURNS. GREAT COSTUME, SIR.

ER, THANKS, Y'ALL.

EGADS! THIS CRETIN THINKS I'M ONE OF HIS PEERS! WHAT DO I *DO?* WHAT DO I *SAY?* MUST TRY TO RESPOND AS AN *ORDINARY PERSON.*

PFFT! HE *STILL* CAN'T REMEMBER MY NAME.

OOPS!

...SPEAK TO ME, HOMER!

WAIT. I THINK HE'S FINALLY BEGINNING TO STIR.

LOOK! HIS EYES ARE OPENING!

OH, DR. HIBBERT, THANK GOODNESS HE'S ALRIGHT!

WHU?...WH-WHERE AM I? WHO ARE YOU PEOPLE? WHAT'S GOING ON HERE?

HOMER, IT'S ME, MARGE...

MARGE SIMPSON...

YOUR WIFE!

MY WIFE? LOOK LADY, I'VE NEVER SEEN YOU BEFORE IN MY LIFE.

HOLD ON A MINUTE. MAYBE I SHOULD PLAY ALONG. SHE'S A STONE COLD FOX! AND THAT HAIR--!GRRROWL!!

BUT, HOMEY, YOU'VE GOT TO REMEMBER ME. WE'VE BEEN TOGETHER SINCE HIGH SCHOOL... WE HAVE THREE KIDS... A MORTGAGE...

MRS. SIMPSON, IT APPEARS THAT HOMER'S HEAD TRAUMA HAS RESULTED IN AMNESIA. IT MIGHT BE BEST NOT TO TAX HIS BRAIN ALL AT ONCE WITH TOO MUCH INFORMATION ABOUT HIS LIFE...ESPECIALLY ANYTHING CONCERNING THE BEE-OH-WHY.

THE BOY? !URK! THE BOY? !ACK! WHO IS THIS !GAH! BOY?

SEE WHAT I MEAN?

PERHAPS WE SHOULD STEP OUTSIDE AND DISCUSS THIS WHILE YOUR HUSBAND GETS SOME REST.

WHAT'S WRONG WITH ME? WHY CAN'T I REMEMBER WHO I AM? THAT LADY SAYS I'M HER HUSBAND, BUT HOW DO I KNOW SHE'S TELLING THE TRUTH?

I NEED SOME HARD FACTS FROM A RELIABLE SOURCE OF INFORMATION THAT'S NOT GOING TO JERK ME AROUND. LIKE THAT IMPULSE BUYING NETWORK ON T.V.

HEY, WHAT'S THIS?

THE SPRINGFIELD FREE PRESS

"RADIOACTIVE MAN" CLOBBERS COLOSSUS

NOW DOGGONE IT, RALPHIE, YOU'VE GOTTA STOP CALLING HERE EVERY TIME YOU GET SOMETHING STUCK IN AN *ELECTRICAL SOCKET*. THAT'S WHY GOD MADE *SCREW DRIVERS*. NOW LEAVE DADDY ALONE, SON. I'VE GOT A LOT OF *IMPORTANT* POLICE WORK TO DO.

CHIEF WIGGUM, IS THAT YOU?

RALPH? WHAT'S HAPPENED TO YOUR *VOICE* BOY? HAVE YOU BEEN SNACKING ON MOMMY'S *MAKE-UP* AGAIN?

I'M NOT YOUR SON, CHIEF! IT'S *MARGE SIMPSON*!

OH, HIYA MARGE. TROUBLE WITH THE BOY AGAIN?

I'M AFRAID IT'S *MY HUSBAND* THIS TIME. HE THINKS HE'S *RADIOACTIVE MAN*, AND HE'S HEADING DOWNTOWN...

ξCHOMP, CHOMPξ

HELLO...CHIEF, ARE YOU LISTENING? HELLO...

ξSMACK, SLURPξ

I HEAR CHEWING SOUNDS.

WE'LL GET RIGHT ON IT!

WE'RE GONNA HAVE TO CANCEL OUR PLANE TICKETS TO *RENO*, BOYS. HOMER SIMPSON IS ON A RAMPAGE, AND HE'S *RADIOACTIVE!*

HMMM...SOMETHING TELLS ME WE SHOULD GET IN THE CAR AND GO AFTER HIM OURSELVES.

MAYBE I SHOULD TAKE A QUICK LOOK AT THIS TELEGRAM FIRST.

OH, MY LORD! IT'S FROM *GRAMPA!* HE FELL ASLEEP ON A BUS THAT WAS BRINGING THE RETIREMENT CASTLE RESIDENTS HOME FROM A FIELD TRIP TO THE MYLANTA BOTTLING PLANT! HE SLEPT UNTIL IT REACHED ITS NEXT DESTINATION...

EL SALVADOR!

MEANWHILE, ON THE MEAN STREETS OF SPRINGFIELD...

STAY FROSTY BOYS. THIS MAY BE THE MOST *DANGEROUS* MISSION WE'VE EVER TACKLED.

PRIORITY A-1 IS TO LOCATE THE MONSTER AND THEN RADIO IN FOR BACK-UP.

DO NOT--I REPEAT, DO *NOT* ATTEMPT TO SUBDUE THE BEHEMOTH ON YOUR OWN...

...JUST MONITOR HIS POSITION AND WAIT FOR THE HEAVY FIREPOWER TO ARRIVE!

UP AHEAD THERE, EDDIE. CHECK IT OUT.

I SEE HIM, LOU.

YOU THE RADIOACTIVE MAN?

YES.

YES, I AM.

GET IN THE CAR.

...AND WHATEVER YOU DO, STAY CLEAR OF HIS *ATOMIC FIRE-BREATH!*

YOU WANNA TELL HIM?

NOT ON YOUR LIFE. IT WOULD BE TOO BIG A DISAPPOINTMENT.

BESIDES, ONCE THE CHIEF'S HAD HIS AFTERNOON NAP, HE'LL THINK IT WAS JUST A BAD DREAM BROUGHT ON BY *RANCID DOUGHNUT GREASE* AND *DAY OLD COFFEE.*

CUT IT OUT! YOU'RE MAKING ME *HUNGRY!*

WHAT DO YOU WANNA DO WITH CAPE-BOY?

LET'S TAKE HIM OVER TO *NEW BEDLAM.* THEY'LL KNOW WHAT TO DO WITH HIM.

MINUTES LATER...

HERE WE ARE, BIG GUY...YOUR NEW "CONTAINMENT DOME." HEH, HEH, HEH!

NEW BEDLAM REST HOME FOR THE EMOTIONALLY INTERESTING

:CHUCKLE: GOOD ONE, EDDIE.

WE'VE GOT ANOTHER *LIVE* ONE FOR YOU, DOC.

THIS GUY THINKS HE'S A *SUPER-HERO.*

I AM A SUPER-HERO.

AH, BRING HIM RIGHT IN OFFICERS.

PLEASE, HAVE A SEAT, MR...?

RADIOACTIVE MAN.

UH, YES, OF COURSE. RADIOACTIVE MAN. I SHOULD HAVE RECOGNIZED YOU FROM YOUR VARIOUS FUNNY BOOKS, KEY FOBS AND WHAT-NOT.

WELL NOW, LET'S SEE WHO YOU ARE UNDER THAT *MASK.* BOYS, WOULD YOU BE SO KIND...

HUH?

C'MON BUDDY, QUIT STRUGGLIN'!

YEAH, MAKE IT *EASY* ON YOURSELF. WE'LL TAKE YOUR WHOLE BLASTED *HEAD* OFF IF WE HAVE TO!

:GRUNT: MUST...KEEP MASK...*ON!*

:OOOF: SECRET IDENTITY... MUSTN'T BE... *REVEALED!*

:URK: NEED...*HEAD* TO...*STAY ALIVE!*

:SIGH: ALRIGHT BOYS, LET'S ALLOW HIM TO KEEP THE MASK ON FOR NOW. TAKE HIM DOWN TO THE *DELUSIONS OF GRANDEUR* WARD. I THINK THERE'S AN EMPTY ROOM NEXT TO *BUDDHA.*

SOON, AT 742 EVERGREEN TERRACE...

DON'T WORRY ABOUT A THING, MA'AM. YOUR HUSBAND WILL *ONLY* HAVE TO STAY AT THE NUT HOUSE UNTIL HE ISN'T *CRAZY* ANYMORE.

HOMER IS *NOT* CRAZY. HE JUST HAS *AMNESIA!*

⊰KHHK⊱ ONE ADAM TWELVE, ONE ADAM TWELVE, SEE THE HELPLESS ELDERLY MAN AT FIFTH AND MAIN. POSSIBLE 211 IN PROGRESS. ⊰KHHK⊱

DE-PANTSING! LET'S *ROLL*, LOU!

THOSE STUPID POLICE!

INSTEAD OF BRINGING YOUR FATHER *HOME* OR TAKING HIM TO A *HOSPITAL* THEY HAD HIM COMMITTED TO THE *INSANE ASYLUM.*

SLAM!

NOW WHAT?

WHO KNOWS HOW LONG IT'LL TAKE FOR HIM TO GET HIS MEMORY BACK IN *THAT* PLACE. IN THE MEANTIME, WE NEED *MONEY.*

WHAT ABOUT OUR *SAVINGS ACCOUNT?*

IT'S NEARLY EMPTY. YOUR GRAMPA DIDN'T SAY EXACTLY WHERE HE WAS IN EL SALVADOR, SO I HAD TO PAY A PRIVATE DETECTIVE *A THOUSAND DOLLARS* TO FIND HIM AND BRING HIM HOME.

PFFT! I WOULD HAVE DONE IT FOR *HALF* THAT!

LATER, AT THE SPRINGFIELD NUCLEAR POWER PLANT...

...SO YOU SEE MR. SMITHERS, UNTIL HOMER IS RELEASED I'M GOING TO HAVE TO GET A JOB, AND I WAS WONDERING IF MAYBE MY OLD POSITION HERE AT THE PLANT IS AVAILABLE.

HMM...NO, NOT SINCE WE PROMOTED *GUMMY JOE.* I'M AFRAID THE ONLY OPENING WE HAVE IS FOR YOUR HUSBAND'S JOB. IT'S YOURS IF YOU WANT IT.

BUT I HAVEN'T GOT THE FAINTEST *IDEA* HOW TO DO HOMER'S JOB.

HERE, JUST WATCH THIS SURVEILLANCE TAPE OF YOUR HUSBAND IN ACTION. YOU SHOULD HAVE NO PROBLEM GETTING THE HANG OF IT.

YO, FELLOW COMICS FANS -- BART SIMPSON HERE! HAVE YOU NOTICED LATELY HOW COMIC BOOKS ARE FULL OF NOTHING BUT GRIM AND GRITTY STORIES ABOUT NEGATIVE ROLE-MODELS ENGAGED IN VIOLENT ANTI-SOCIAL BEHAVIOR, USUALLY RESULTING IN GRAPHIC PORTRAYALS OF DEATH AND/OR DISMEMBERMENT? PRETTY COOL, ISN'T IT? BUT AS MOST MEMBERS OF GENERATION X KNOW, COOL CAN BE VERY DEPRESSING. THEREFORE, I DECIDED IT WAS MY DUTY TO SHARE WITH YOU MY INSIGHTS ON HOW TO MAKE THIS HOBBY MORE FUN. MY FIRST TIP -- BUY LOTS OF BONGO COMICS! SECONDLY -- ATTEND YOUR LOCAL COMIC BOOK CONVENTION. BUT BEFORE YOU GO, BE SURE TO READ THIS --

THE OFFICIAL BONGO COMICS
COMIC CONVENTION
SURVIVAL GUIDE

THE MANY TYPES OF FANS

Meeting your fellow fans is half the fun of a convention. Study these profiles of common categories to better understand and interact with them.

THE ZOMBIE	THE GNARLY DUDE	THE SCI-FI FAN	THE ROLE-PLAYER	THE SPECULATOR

THE ZOMBIE — CAPT. SQUID STINKS -- I JUST BUY IT TO KEEP MY COLLECTION COMPLETE.

COLLECTION INCLUDES: Recently completed set of *Millie the Model*.
WHAT'S ON HIS MIND: Should I rent another apartment just to store my comics?

THE GNARLY DUDE — WHOA! AWESOME CHAIN-MAIL BIKINI!

COLLECTION INCLUDES: Dog-eared sword-and-sorcery comics, beer-stained undergrounds.
WHAT'S ON HIS MIND: When Conan cuts some dude's head off with an axe, why don't they show more blood?

THE SCI-FI FAN — ACTUALLY, I PREFER THE TERM "S-F."

COLLECTION INCLUDES: A Q-Tip once used by Leonard Nimoy.
WHAT'S ON HIS MIND: Just what are the theoretical underpinnings of warp drive?

THE ROLE-PLAYER — MY NAME IS LEWIS, BUT YOU CAN CALL ME "DUNGEON MASTER KELZOR."

COLLECTION INCLUDES: An overflowing shelf of fantasy paperbacks, *Dr. Strange* comics.
WHAT'S ON HIS MIND: Does wearing this cloak make me look like an even bigger nerd than I really am?

THE SPECULATOR — READ COMICS?! I'M TOO BUSY MEMORIZING THE LATEST PRICE GUIDE UPDATE.

COLLECTION INCLUDES: Ten copies of the hot new die-cut, gold foil *Green Manta #1* - still poly-bagged.
WHAT'S ON HIS MIND: Should I buy ten more copies?

HEY, FANS!

CHECK OUT THESE PROVOCATIVE PANEL TOPICS:

Lionel Hutz, Attorney at Law explains "How To Sue Your Mom For Throwing Out All Your Old Comics"

Who's Stronger, Radioactive Man, Radiation Dude or the new amalgamated character, Radioactive Duck of the New Fantastic Sub-Atomic Free-Masons?

Cover Enhancements: Now that they've been exposed as worthless, gimmicky marketing come-ons, should recycling be attempted, or should they just go out with the garbage? (free holo-foil comic to first 250 attendees!)

DON'T MISS THE EVER-POPULAR COSTUME CONTEST

Where fans get a chance to display their creativity, originality, and sewing ability, among other things.*

*Note to would-be entrants: skin-tight spandex probably won't look as good on you as it does on your favorite character.

PROS AND CONS:

WHILE YOU'RE AT THE CONVENTION, YOU'LL WANT TO MEET THE MANY PROFESSIONALS IN ATTENDANCE. HERE ARE SOME CLUES TO HELP YOU SPOT THEM.

THE ROOKIE
S DONE UNCREDITED BACKGROUND
INKS ON THREE BOOKS YOU'VE
NEVER HEARD OF

EAD FILLED WITH
REAMS OF FAME,
FORTUNE AND
USCULAR GUYS IN
KINTIGHT SUITS

RFLIES IN
CH CAUSED
OSPECT OF
G HIS IDOLS

OF DISORGANIZED
BROUGHT IN HOPES
FINDING WORK

CALLUSES CAUSED BY
RACTICING SIGNING HIS NAME
IN CASE SOMEONE ASKS FOR
HIS AUTOGRAPH

THE OLD PRO
HAS MET 2,361 CONSECUTIVE DEADLINES

HEAD FILLED WITH
RESENTMENT OVER
INFLATED EARNINGS
OF TODAY'S STARS

HEART WARMED BY
MEMORIES OF "THE
GOOD OLD DAYS"

PAGES OF ORIGINAL ART,
WON AFTER YEARS OF
BITTER STRUGGLE WITH
PUBLISHER

ULCER CAUSED BY
2,361 CONSECUTIVE
DEADLINES

THE STAR
HIS METEORIC RISE HAS AMAZED US ALL

PRETENDING TO HIDE
BEHIND EXPENSIVE
SUNGLASSES, BUT WILL
BE HURT IF YOU DON'T
RECOGNIZE HIM

OFFICIAL LICENSED
EARRING

OFFICIAL LICENSED
T-SHIRT

OFFICIAL LICENSED
UNDERWEAR

THIS MONTH'S
ROYALTIES

THE STAR'S ENTOURAGE
(NOT SHOWN):
• MANAGER
• INVESTMENT ADVISER
• BODYGUARDS
• PERSONAL TRAINER
• PUBLICIST
• DRIVER
• FOOD TASTER
• THE GUYS WHO
ACTUALLY DO THE WRITING
AND DRAWING NOW THAT
THE STAR NO LONGER
HAS TIME IN HIS
BUSY SCHEDULE

YOU KNOW THE 4 BASIC
VENTION FOOD GROUPS? **CHIPS•COLA•FRENCH FRIES•PIZZA** BE SURE TO GET AT LEAST TWO SERVINGS
FROM EACH GROUP DAILY

O YOU WANT TO BE A CARTOONIST?

ny would-be artists bring samples of their work to conventions with the hopes of
getting a valuable critique from one of the attending pros. Unfortunately, these
easoned veterans often speak in industry jargon, making their comments hard
to understand. In hopes of clarifying this situation, we present translations
of some commonly used phrases.

WHEN HE SAYS:

YOU NEED TO WORK ON YOUR STORYTELLING.

PAY ATTENTION TO THE SPOTTING OF BLACKS.

YOU'VE JUMPED THE LINE AND VIOLATED THE 180 DEGREE RULE.

INTERESTING ANATOMY.

HE MEANS:

HOW LONG TILL WE BREAK FOR LUNCH?

WHERE'S THE MEN'S ROOM?

WHEN IS THE DISTRIBUTOR'S COCKTAIL PARTY?

CHECK THE BABE IN THE VAMPIRELLA COSTUME!

DON'T FORGET ABOUT
SHOPPING!

This useful economic model can help you judge
the moment you'll get the best bargain.

BEGINNING OF CONVENTION — END OF CONVENTION

SUPPLY

DEALER ANXIETY

$$\frac{\text{TIME REMAINING}}{\text{SUPPLY}} \times \frac{1}{\text{DEALER ANXIETY}} = \text{PRICE}$$

WARNING TO
FEMALE FANS!

E CONVENTION ATTENDEES OUTNUMBER
ALES BY APPROXIMATELY 99 TO 1. MOST
E SINGLE, ADOLESCENT AND DEVOID OF
AL SKILLS. YOU MAY WISH TO LEARN THE
TIONS OF THE NEAREST EMERGENCY EXIT.

CONVENTION
PREPARATION CHECKLIST
REMEMBER THESE ESSENTIALS:

☐ **WANT LIST**
☐ **CASH**
☐ **CHECKS**
☐ **CREDIT CARDS**
☐ **AUTOGRAPH BOOK**
☐ **TAKE SHOWER!!!**